ZIG AND Z IN Yer FACE missus!

A MESSAGE FROM THE AUTHORS:

ZAG "School doesn't have to end at 4 o'clock! That's why we've written this book. It's highly educational with lots of big words and no pictures whatsoever. It's also crammed with lots of boring facts and figures that you can learn off_ Enjoy!"

ZIG "Four pints of silver top, Mr. Milkman, please!"

B⊟XTREE

First published in 1994 by Boxtree Limited,
Broadwall House, 21 Broadwall, London SE1 9PL

Copyright © Double Z Enterprises 1994
Licensed by Copyright Promotions Limited

ISBN 1 85283 386 6

10 9 8 7 6 5 4 3 2 1

CONTENTS

IN Yer FACE

STAR PROFILE

ZIG

NAME: Zigmund Ambrose Zogly

ADDRESS: 10 Zogland Heights, Zog 15, Planet Zog

HEIGHT: 2ft 15" (I'm taler than my brother - so there!)

HOBBIES: collecting hobbies

FAVOURITE FOOD: Garlic and chocolate paté & marmalade in a toasted sandwich.

FAVOURITE SINGER: Myself, because I'm quite good really, and I'll probably be in a live pop group like Depeche Mauve when I grow up!

FAVOURITE ACTOR: Fred Flintstone and James Bond.

FAVOURITE ACTRESS: Florence from The Magic Roundabout.

FAVOURITE SONG: "My brother pongs" - a song that I did write by my own self.

FAVOURITE BAND: St. Zogatious school brass band - cause I play a mean triangle!

FAVOURITE FILM: Fuji 35mm!

MOST EMBARRASSING MOMENT: Once I got sick on the bus and it did roll all the way up the front!

GIRLFRIENDS NAME: Excuse me, but I don't have a girlfriend! I don't mind holding hands - but I won't do kissing! And besides I have a train set and you have to talk to gurls!!

BEST FRIEND: Hillary - you'll understand that in a moment! Huh! huh! huh!

FAVOURITE SAYING: "IN YER FACE, MISSUS!"

STAR PROFILE

ZAG

NAME: Zagnatious Hillary Zogly

ADDRESS: Top bunk in the same house as Ziggidy bo!

HOBBIES: Dating supermodels

HEIGHT: 6ft 3'..oops, for a moment I thought I was Dolph Lundgren..easy mistake to make!!

FAVOURITE SINGER: Me and Raggazagga -which is me aswell!

FAVOURITE FOOD: Mushroom and Lemon curd quiche

FAVOURITE BANDS: Jeff Leppard and his band, RATM and any Trash mental with loud guitar music!!

FAVOURITE SONG: "Knockin on Kevin's Door." by Guns with Roses.

FAVOURITE ACTOR: Arnie

FAVOURITE ACTRESS: Tia Carrere and Patricia Arquette

FAVOURITE FILM: The Star Wars trilogy and Jurazig park.

GIRLFRIENDS NAME: What? All 750 of them?!

MOST EMBARRASSING MOMENT: Being an hour late on my first date with Cindy Crawford!

FAVOURITE SAYING: "I'm going to tell mother, Zigmund

BEST FRIEND: Zig, I suppose, even though he's completely mad in the head!

ah ? duh ..a er but um ... er
AN OPINION!

THESE MY DEAR READERS ARE THE KIND OF STATEMENTS THAT LET PEOPLE KNOW THAT YOU HAVE AN OPINION AND ARE A CLEVER KIND OF MODERN THINKING, WITH-IT GUY OR GAL. I MEAN, HOW DO YOU THINK I GOT ON TELLY? I HAD AN OPINION OF COURSE, AND A DOWNRIGHT FINE ONE AT THAT!
HERE ARE TWO DAY TO DAY OPINION BUSTERS THAT YOU CAN USE AT YOUR LEISURE. ITS MY GIFT TO YOU - OPINION PUPILS!

① WHEN ASKED "What do you think of the Scellini hi-fi system?"
JUST ANSWER:
"Ah, the Scellini XJ-5000 quadrophonic surround sound hifi system is a jolly fine piece of midi equipment made and developed in Italy by Mr. Poliano Scellini. The sound quality is excellent with a superb bass booster capability and ten preset graphic equaliser. It also boasts of a state of the art surround sound, pro logic system and a mini-disc with recordable capabilities. Certainly one of the finest and most reasonably priced mid-range, low price stereo systems available!"

② WHEN ASKED "What do you think of the current Thrash metal scene?"
YOU CAN ANSWER:
"Well, to be honest the Thrash scene leaves me a tad cold these days, Metallica are good but they've lost a bit of their integrity by going a bit too mainstream. But bands like Pantera and Prong with their exciting live shows and raw unashamedly brash albums have managed to keep the spirit of Thrash alive and in so avoid letting it drown under the immense weight of the Seattle and American Indie onslaught!"

SPECIAL NOTE: ☆

WASHO WASHING POWDER, THE SCELLINI XJ-5000 HOME ENTERTAINMENT SYSTEM AND THE BOOK "THRASH MENTAL THROUGHOUT THE 90'S" ARE ALL AVAILABLE THROUGH THE "ZAG IS GREAT AND I AGREE!" FAN CLUB AT SPECIAL MEMBERSHIP RATES. WHILE STOCKS LAST.

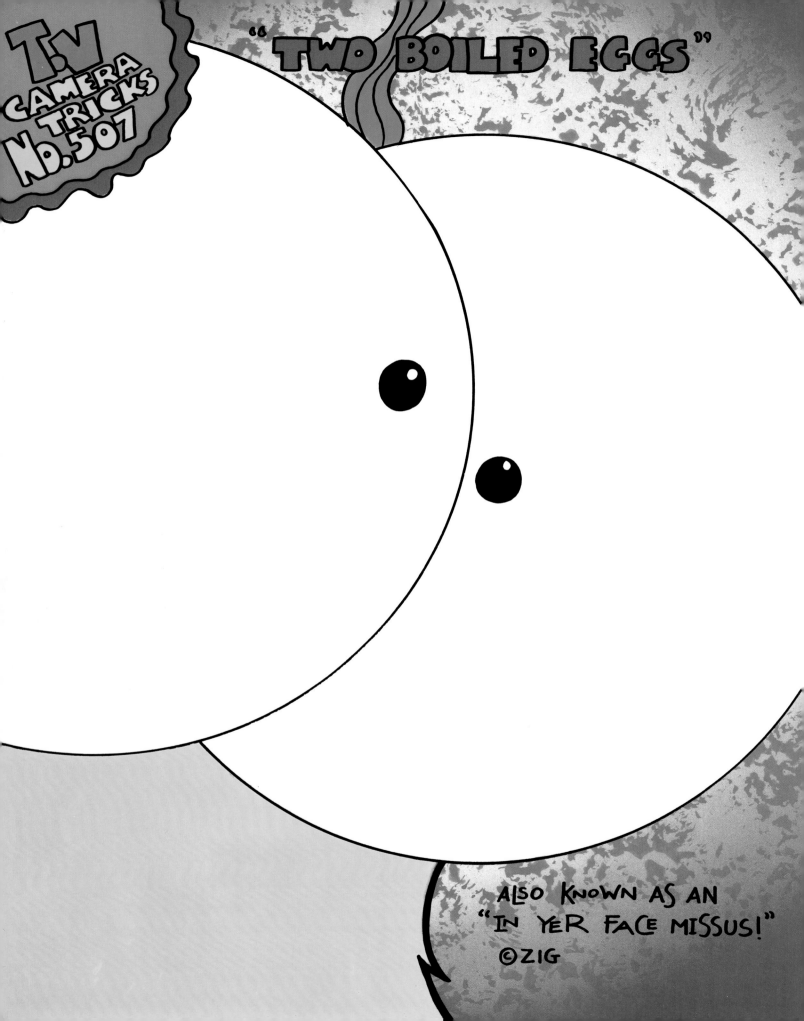

AND NOW THE STORY OF..

Little Red
TERMINATOR

Once upon a time, not so long ago, in a place not so far away from here, a little girl set off on a little journey...

HI, ME AGAIN!

The little girl was known as little Red, because she always wore red.

IT'S A FASHION THING; A STATEMENT OF MY INDIVIDUALITY; BESIDES THAT WHOLE SEATTLE LOOK IS OUT!

She was on her way to visit her Granny who lived in the middle of the forest...

WELL, SHE USED TO...

..BEFORE THEY PULLED THE FOREST DOWN AND BUILT GRIMM CITY.

GRIMM CITY

NOW SHE LIVES IN APARTMENT 207 OLD MOTHER HUBBARD HIGH RISE.

It was a dangerous journey through Grimm city, so Red decided to call a cab.

HELLO, PIG CABS...

PIG CAB

..CAN YOU TAKE ME TO OLD MOTHER HUBBARD HIGH RISE? GOOD, I'M AT TREE PHONE 75.

Unbeknownst to Red, some mischief was afoot..

AFOOT

7-5

JACK MOTHER PEEP

AH-HA!

CAB

FISHBONE

TAKE HER THE LONG WAY 'ROUND AND TAKE FIFTY BUCKS FOR YOUR TROUBLE!

KNOCK KNOCK

DON'T WORRY, THE ONLY PORRIDGE SHE'LL BE DOING FROM NOW ON IS BEHIND BARS!

OH, OH, THIS IS MY BIT!

KNOCK KNOCK

WHO'S THERE?

IT'S ONLY ME, LITTLE RED

ER...OK...COME ON IN, MR WOLF

SCRIPT

OK, OK STOP EVERYTHING! ZIG, YOU'RE NOT SUPPOSED TO KNOW IT'S THE WOLF!

BUT I KNOW IT IS!

HOW COULD YOU KNOW? THE DOOR'S CLOSED!

DIRECTOR

IT SAYS IN THE SCRIPT... "WOLF PRETENDS TO BE LITTLE RED!"

OH...LOOK, JUST PRETEND YOU DON'T KNOW OK?

OK, I'LL PRETEND, LIKE YOU PRETEND YOU KNOW CLAUDIA SCHIFFER WHEN YOU DON'T EVEN KNOW WHO SHE IS...

LOOK, JUST GET ON WITH IT!

ER...COME IN, LITTLE RED WOLF!

OH!!

A few hours later, way behind schedule, Little Red arrived at Granny's

I CAN'T WAIT TO SEE GRAN'S FACE WHEN I GIVE HER THESE NEW VIDEOS, ESPECIALLY THIS RUDE ONE ABOUT "TAKE THAT" IN THE NUDIES : "HOWARD'S END"

KNOCK KNOCK

WHO'S THERE?

IT'S LITTLE RED, GRAN!

WELL COME ON IN, MY DEAR.

And so, little Red slowly pushed open the door to see Granny tucked up snugly in bed.

YO, GRAN!

Whirrrrr *KACHUNK*

YIKES!!

HASTA LA VISTA VOLFIE!

NOT SO FAST LITTLE RED!

WHO ARE YOU?

IT'S ME!

ROBOGRAN

COOO-EL COSTUME ZIG

YOU SHOULDN'T HAVE LOCKED ME IN THE CLOSET, MR WOLF... IT MAKES ME ANGRY!

NOW WHAT SHALL WE DO WITH THE WOLF IN THE NIGHTDRESS?

DON'T WORRY, I'VE GOT THE PERFECT PUNISHMENT!

IMPRESSING GURLS

on that first date!

by Mr. LoVeZag

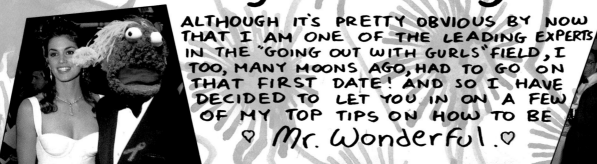

ALTHOUGH IT'S PRETTY OBVIOUS BY NOW THAT I AM ONE OF THE LEADING EXPERTS IN THE "GOING OUT WITH GURLS" FIELD, I TOO, MANY MOONS AGO, HAD TO GO ON THAT FIRST DATE! AND SO I HAVE DECIDED TO LET YOU IN ON A FEW OF MY TOP TIPS ON HOW TO BE ♡ Mr. Wonderful. ♡

A. SMELLS:

UNFORTUNATELY GOING OUT WITH GURLS CAN MEAN HAVING TO TAKE A BATH! BUT, MY DEAR FRIENDS, SUCH DRASTIC MEASURES CAN BE AVOIDED BY LIBERALLY DOLLOPING ON MY PATENTED COLOGNE "MUSK DU ZAG" (only £17·95 a bottle, available from the "Zag is great and I agree" Fan club.) YOU'LL SMELL LIKE YOU'VE NEVER SMELT BEFORE!

BUT WHAT ABOUT THOSE REALLY STINKY ARMPITS? EASY. STICK A COUPLE OF THOSE BLUE OR GREEN (Depending on your outfit!) LOO FRESHENERS UNDER YOUR PONGY PITS!

B. CLOTHES

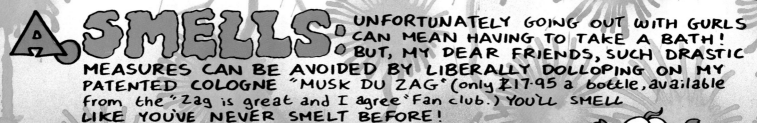

Demon-stration

HERE'S MY GUARANTEED KNOCK 'EM DEAD FASHION TIP: FIRSTLY, DO YOUR HOMEWORK. FIND OUT IF SHE HAS ANY SPECIAL INTERESTS; SPORTS, ARTS AND CRAFTS ETC. AND THEN SIMPLY DRESS TO IMPRESS!

CJ PRESENTS

ONCE AGAIN DO YOUR HOMEWORK. IT IS IMPORTANT TO BUY A PRESENT TO SUIT YOUR DATE. HERE ARE THREE SIMPLE RULES THAT I ALWAYS USE:
IF SHE'S SWEET, BUY HER SOME SWEETS!
IF SHE'S DELIGHTFUL, BUY HER SOME TURKISH DELIGHT!
IF SHE'S PALE, BUY HER A BUCKET!

CORRECT ✓

OH NOOO! NOT TURKISH DELIGHT AGAIN!

SEXY LOOK No.5

INCORRECT ✗

HERE'S MY ODOUR EATER COLLECTION, I DIDN'T BOTHER WRAPPING THEM!

WELL, AT LEAST IT'S NOT TURKISH DELIGHT!

WELL, NOW YOU SMELL GOOD, YOU LOOK HOT AND YOU'VE GOT A PRESSIE THAT WILL IMPRESS. IT'S TIME FOR D-DAY. LET'S SEE HOW YOU'D GET ON. THE FOLLOWING TEST WAS DEVISED BY MYSELF AND DR. RUTH AND HAS BEEN CLINICALLY TESTED (but not on animals 'cause that's downright cruel and not the sort of thing clever, nice upstanding people would do—we tested it on Zig instead!) ALL YOU'VE GOT TO DO IS MARK OFF A) B) OR C) AND THEN YOU CAN SEE HOW GOOD A FIRST DATE YOU ARE!

ON YOUR FIRST DATE YOU BRING HER TO:

A) THE DEVON SNOT FLINGING FESTIVAL.

B) THE ANNUAL TRACTOR PARTS SWAP SHOP.

C) A POSH RESTAURANT.

IF YOU GO TO A RESTAURANT DO YOU ORDER:

A) FISH AND CHIPS.

B) LE COQ SPORTIF.

C) NO. 47.

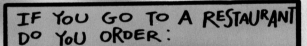

ANSWER

A) 'cause snot flinging can be fun and besides posh restaurants are, quite frankly, too dear! Not B) either because no one ever swaps their dual converter for a '76 Massey!

DATE CITY

ANSWER

A) Because fish and chips are cheap, nutritious and you can eat them standing up so there's no embarrassing moments with cutlery. Not B) 'cause it's an aftershave and not C) 'cause the No.47 is a bus!

DRESS YOUR DREAMDATES

SIMPLY CUT OUT THE CLOTHES OF YOUR CHOICE AND DRESS YOUR DATE TO MAKE YOUR DREAMS COME TRUE!

KILT

MONACLE TO LOOK SOPHIS!

YACHT DECK SHOES

NICOLAS CAGE SNAKESKIN BOOTS

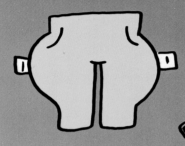

JODPHURS

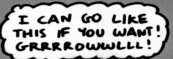

I CAN GO LIKE THIS IF YOU WANT! GRRRROWWLLL!

CALVIN KLEIN POLO NECK

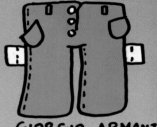

GIORGIO ARMANI JEANS

AN ANGUS DEAYTON WING COLLAR SHIRT

PILOTS CAP

TOP HAT

RAGGA FLOPPY HAT

RIDING HAT

DEER STALKER

EAU DE ZAG

ZAG SAVAGE AFTERSHAVE

ZAG D'AMOUR FUR-FUME

NECKTIE

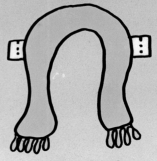

SILK SCARF

HEAD WEAR:

TOILET ROLL

A BANANA

FISH

SHEEP

ANOTHER BANANA

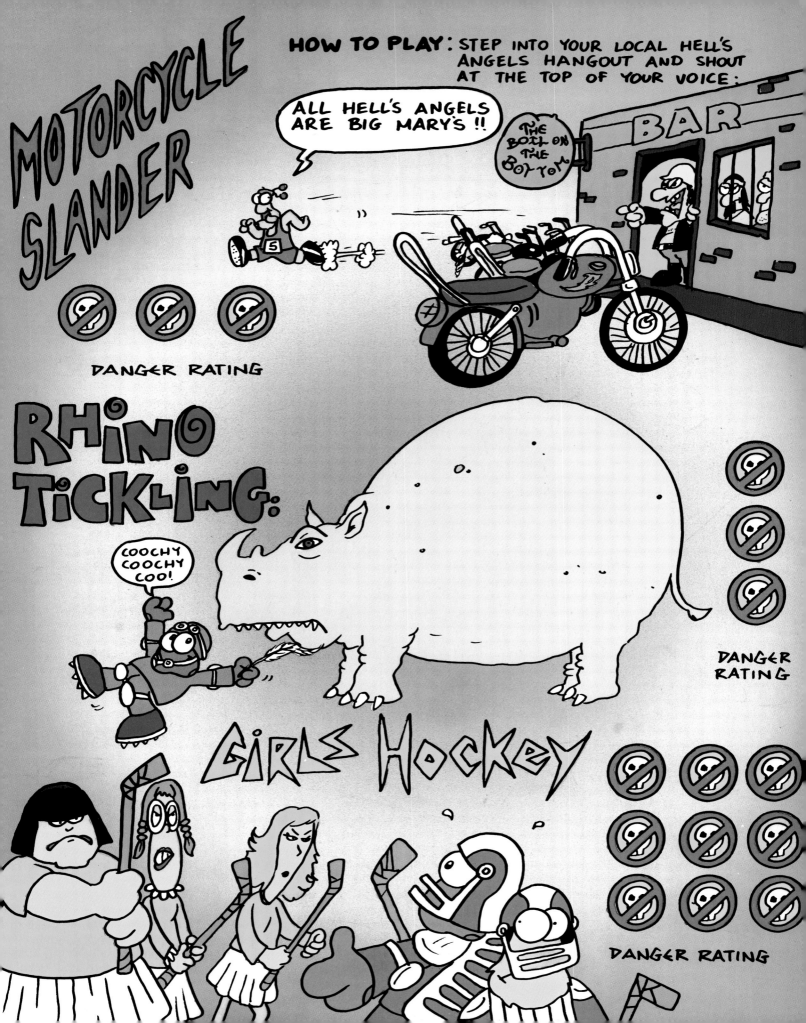

WORDs THAT RHyme With ORANGE

BORANGE!

WHAT ON EARTH IS HE SAYING?

THAT'S BETTER!

TRANSLATION

CALLING ALL SUPERHEROES, GODZILLA IS EATING TOKYO. WE NEED HELP.. THIS IS THE MAYOR SPEAKING!

HELLO, MAYOR... I THINK WE CAN HELP

THANK YOU... BUT WHO ARE YOU??

IT'S US, SOCKMAN AND BUNION BOY. SUPERHEROES OF CHIROPODY!

ZIG! STOP THIS STORY RIGHT NOW! WHY AM I WEARING AN ONION COSTUME? I'M BUNION BOY! BUNION BOY!!

HOW ON EARTH DID I GET TALKED INTO WEARING THIS RIDICULOUS COSTUME? OF COURSE, I SHOULD HAVE KNOWN THAT YOU WOULDN'T KNOW WHAT A BUNION IS! WELL, YOUNG MAN IT IS **NOT** AN ONION THAT BEGINS WITH A "B". AND IF YOU THINK FOR ONE MINUTE THAT I ....

OH GIVE OVER ZAG! WE'VE GOT TO SAVE TOKYO FOR GOODNESS SAKE!!

WELL, OK THEN... BUT THIS ISN'T THE LAST YOU'VE HEARD ABOUT THIS, YOUNG FELLOW!!

WHO THE HECK IS SOCKMAN??

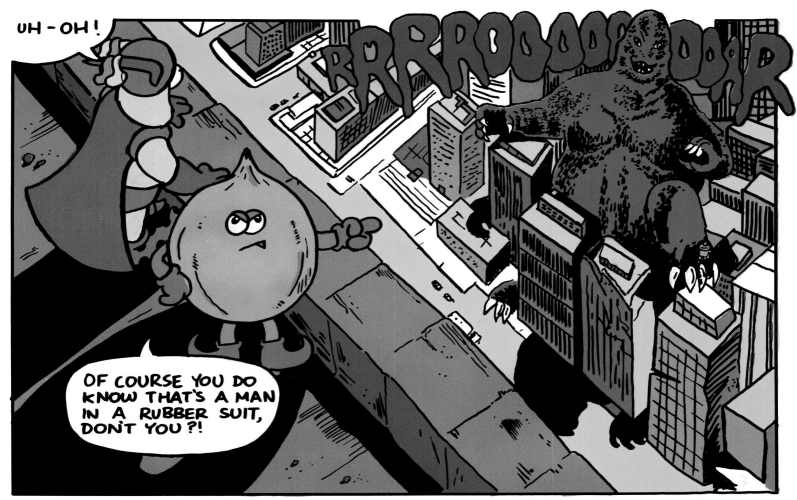

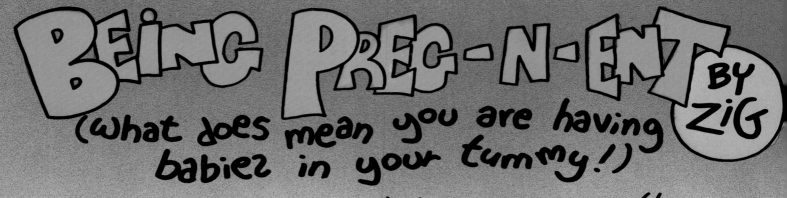

BEING PREG-N-ENT

BY ZIG

(what does mean you are having babiez in your tummy!)

① It is very important that you do have the correct anorak for the baby which you are having.

DEMONSTRATION:

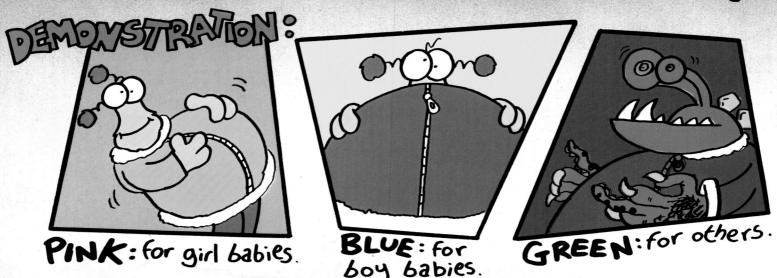

PINK: for girl babies.

BLUE: for boy babies.

GREEN: for others.

② Being Preg-n-ent can mean that you do have very strange foods to eat:

③ Being Preg-n-ent can also mean that you do watch strange programmes on television.

coal sandwiches
Old odour-eater Pizza
Bicycles
Blu-Tak Blancmange

HIGHWAY,
Good morning with
Ann and Nick,
ANYTHING ON
CHANNEL 4.

Here are some things that you probably should not do while being Preg-n-ent:

① BUNJI JUMP
② RAP JUMPING WITH CILLA BLACK
③ STEAL DUCKS FROM YOUR LOCAL POND AND PUT THEM ON YOUR HEAD - ESPECIALLY MALLARDS
④ TALK TO KEITH CHEGWIN

④ When the big day comes, you must have handy;
   A. A BINGO CALLER.
   B. A SUITCASE WITH YOUR PYJAMAS AND COAL SANDWICHE2.
   C. YOUR HUB-STAND AND HIS MIDS-WIFE.

⑤ When your time has come, you will know because you will look like the front end of a Volkswagen Beetle. If you're really quiet you can hear a little voice saying:
"Let me out, let me out. I want to see the world from the outside of my little tummy house!"
Then the Bingo man will shout "HOUSE!" and there will be a big POP sound and everyone will shout "It's a baby, a little baby!" as the baby does fly out at 100 miles per hour and is caught in a big net by the mids-wife. Then you and your lovely baby go on a holiday to Disneyland and everyone is happy!

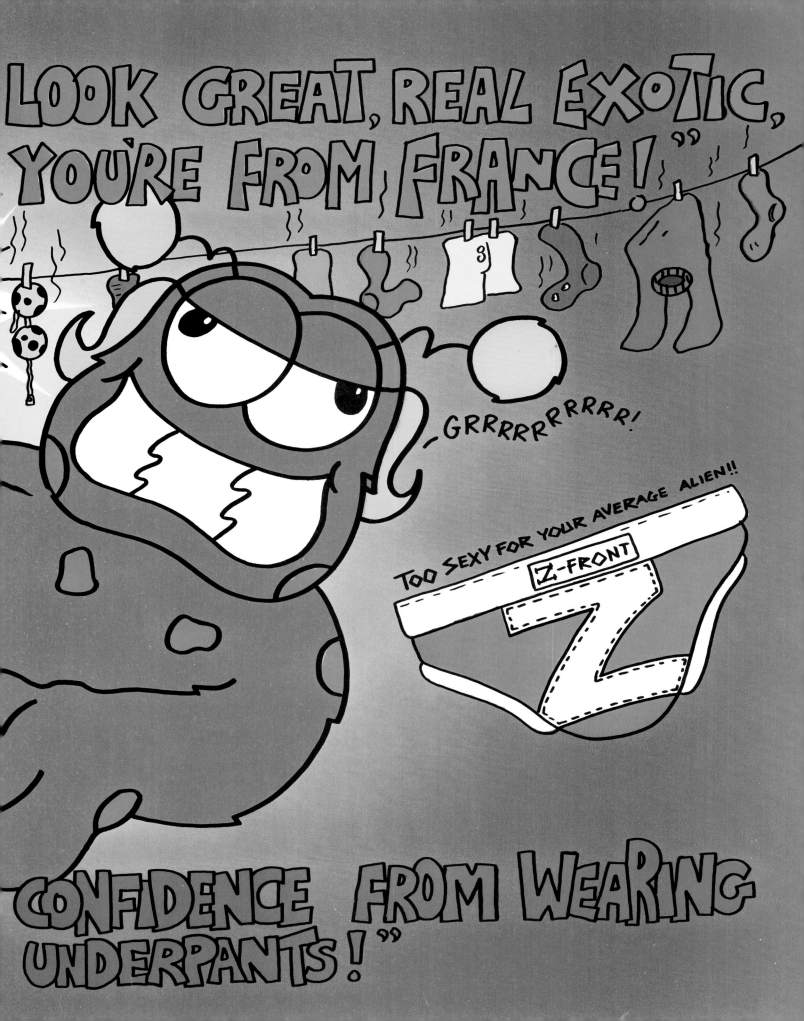

A FILM DOCUMENTARY ABOUT AN AVERAGE WEEKEND WITH AN ABOVE AVERAGE ALIEN.

DIRECTED BY ZAG AND SPIELY

ZAG   SPIEL BERG

©ZAG CORP.

FRIDAY 8pm.

I fly my Lear jet to L.A. with my Teenage Fanclub CD blasting out on my SCELLINI XJ-5000.

keanu picks me up at the airport.

YO ALIEN DUDE!

K WHAT'S HAPPENIN'?

Let the weekend commenc

 ...straight to the Hollywood bowl for Metallica.

Me   Reevsey

ENTER ZAGMAN!

I thought I should teach them a couple of new licks.

NICE AXE WORK ZAGMAN!

THANKS J!

 Midnight barbie on my yacht in Malibu with Pamela Anderson

Up at five in the morning for a workout with Cindy.

2pm business lunch at Skywalker ranch with George Lucas

I DONT CARE IF YOU'RE OFFERIN $58 MILLION. I'M NOT GETTING I THAT DUSTBIN AGAIN!

ZIV

ISSUE NO. 5
NOT FOR SALE TO MINERS!

OH CRIKEY! IT'S ZIG AND HIS Unfeasably large Anorak

OH, NO. HERE HE COMES AGAIN, IT'S THAT CLUMSY TWIT WITH THAT OVERSIZED OVERCOAT!

IT'S AN ANORAK ACTUALLY!

ARE YOU GETTIN' SMART WITH ME? I'LL 'AVE YOU 'ROUND THE BACK OF THE CHIPPER, TONIGHT.. SIX O'CLOCK, BE THERE!

OO-ER!

MY ANORAK'S GOT ME INTO TROUBLE AGAIN! IF ONLY I COULD GET THIS ZIPPER UNSTUCK I COULD BE JUST LIKE NORMAL BOYS!

MEANWHILE

BLIMEY 'ECK, ME BLOOMIN' BRAKES HAVE GONE AND I'M HEADING STRAIGHT FOR SUNNYDALE!

OH CRIKEY, THERE'S A RUNAWAY TRUCK WITH FIFTY TONS OF LARD HEADING STRAIGHT FOR OUR VILLAGE!

DON'T WORRY MR. MAYOR I'LL SAVE OUR VILLAGE!

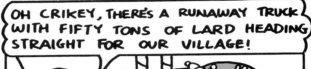

DON'T BE SOFT LAD! WHAT COULD YOU DO?

I CAN ONLY TRY MR. MAYOR!!

IT'S JUST ME AND ME ANORAK NOW!

BLOOMIN' 'ECK, WHAT'S THAT DAFT TWERP DOIN' IN'T MIDDLE O'T ROAD?? HE'S A GONNER FOR SURE!

SQUASH!

BOING

ZAG'S GUIDE TO MAKING MONEY FROM YOUR HOME VIDEOS

HEY, DO YOU WANT TO MAKE ₦1000? OF COURSE YOU DO! WELL, HERE'S HOW; ALL YOU'VE GOT TO DO IS KNOW THE CORRECT METHOD FOR GETTING YOUR HOME VIDEO ON A TV BLOOPER SHOW. HAVE A LOOK AT HOW I CREATED MY MONEY MAKING, REALISTIC LOOKING FILM FUNNIES!!

TV CLIP

Lucky I had the camera rolling at this moment when Zig lost his trunks at the "Funwaterworld" water slide!

WHAT THEY DIDN'T SEE

₦200

Remember to keep your camera at the ready just in case a herd of Rhino break lose as your brother's in the toilet at a Safari Park

₦500

Oh dear it seems that Zig forgot to follow the strict safety harness rules on the roller coaster from Hell.

Y'SEE, IT WAS WORTH IT!

₦1000

AHA! IT HAS VORKED, IT HAS VORKED!!

OK, DOC, NOW LET ME GO ON MY JOURNEY OF DISCOVERY!

VELL OK ZEN, HERE'S YOUR BROTHER'S MOUTH. NOW, OFF YOU GO! I HAVE NO FURTHER USE FOR YOU!

AND SO MY JOURNEY BEGAN!

BRAIN

WELCOME TO ZIG'S BRAIN

WOW!

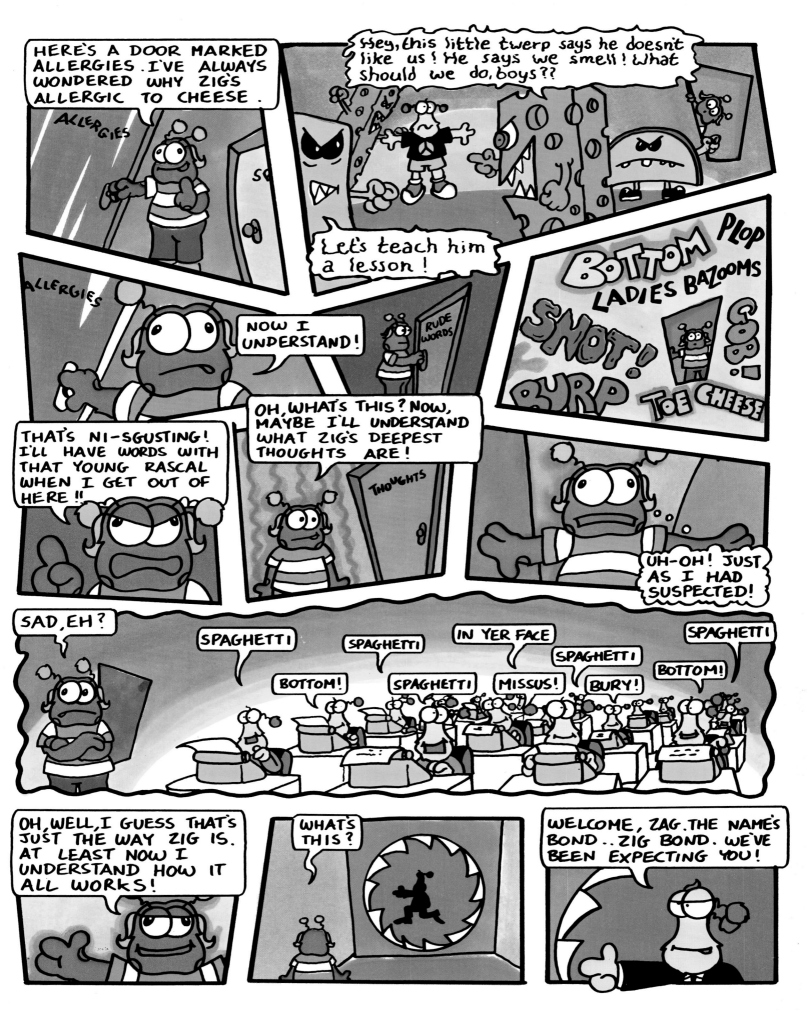

WIPE OUT YOUR PROBLEMS

TOILET MAN

HE GETS TO THE BOTTOM OF EVERY JOB!
Call Freephone ZOG 900.

MAZE
HELP ZIG GET TO THE LAUNDROMAT!

LAUNDRO MAT

ZIG's fun PAGE

FUN GAME:
IF YOU LICK THE SCALP OF A SKINHEAD. IT TICKLES YOUR TONGUE!

Join the dots

Solo Sardines
1. SQUEEZE YOURSELF IN UNDER THE STAIRS!
2. COME OUT WHEN YOU'RE FINISHED.

CROSSWORD.
CLUES:
1 (DOWN) WHAT DO MICE EAT?
2 (DOWN) WHAT IS HARD YOGHURT?
3 (DOWN) WHAT SMELLS LIKE CHEESE?
1 (ACROSS) WHAT AM I ALLERGIC TO?

CLEVER HAND SHADOWS
1 TURN OFF THE LIGHTS.
2 EXCEPT FOR ONE LIGHT.
3 PUT YOUR HANDS TOGETHER.
4 HERE IS PRINCE CHARLES.

Toffee Apple Fur
1 Get some Toffee Apples.
2 Stick them to your fur.

DIFFICULT JIGSAW

JOIN THE DOTS: ITS SPILT JELLY!

CROSSWORD SOLUTION: 1 (DOWN):CHEESE 2 (DOWN):CHEESE 3 (DOWN):CHEESE 1 (ACROSS):CHEESE

I WANT TO BE LIKE ZAG !

WELL, READERS AS YOU KNOW THERE IS ONLY ONE ZAG AND YOU COULD NEVER EVER BE AS COO-EL OR SOPHIS AS HE IS. BUT THEN AGAIN, THERE'S NO BLOOMIN' HARM IN TRYING!

CLOTHING:
ZAG HAS BEEN KNOWN AS A FASHION GOD IN SHOWBIZ CIRCLES AND THE CORRECT CLOTHING IS A STEP NEARER TO BECOMING A ZAGETTE.

HATS:
ZAG LOVES HIS HATS, FROM BASEBALL CAPS TO FEZZES, ONCE THEY'RE EXPENSIVE AND COLOURFUL HE'LL WEAR THEM. AS ZAG ALWAYS SAYS: "wear a happy hat and your head will smile!"

JACKETS:
"I like being noticed. 'Notice' is my middle name." ONE WAY OF BEING NOTICED IS TO INVENT YOUR OWN FASHION, LIKE ZAG DID. "It's called 'Gunge' wear! what you do is stick old bits of rotten fruit and a couple of egg sandwiches in the pockets of your favourite jackets. leave them there for a few months to seep into the cloth and when they've gone all gungey and gooey, go to a party! It's coo-el to wear them to posh dos 'cause you're making your very own fashion statement, you're saying "I'm me, I'm smelly, and I don't bloomin' care!"

SPECIAL HINTS:
ZAG ALSO HAS TWO BARBIE T-SHIRTS, BERMUDA SHORTS, HOODIES, STRIPEY TOPS, CARE BEAR BOXER SHORTS AND A COLLECTION OF DRESSES (for acting purposes only!!) "I also like those jeans with the buttons on them because there's less chance of getting your fur caught in the zipper!"

FOOTWEAR:
FIRSTLY, TO BE LIKE ZAG IN THIS AREA YOU MUST ONLY HAVE ONE PAIR OF 100% NYLON SOCKS THAT YOU WEAR AT ALL TIMES, EVEN IN THE BATH. YOU MUST ALSO BUY TWO PAIRS OF SHOES; A PAIR OF CHUCK'S STARS AND STRIPES OR LEOPARD SKIN PATTERNED AND A PAIR OF YACHTING DECK SHOES.

THE LOOK:
HAIR:
WELL, THERE'S NO TWO WAYS ABOUT IT ZAG FANS, YOU ARE GOING TO HAVE TO DYE THOSE LOCKS. USE ZOG BRAND "ZAG YELLOW" AND "ZAG ORANGE". MIX EVENLY AND LET IT SET FOR A COUPLE OF HOURS.

THEN APPLY SOME ZOG SUPER MOUSSE AND CREATE YOUR OWN FAVOURITE ZAG HAIRSTYLE. THE VARIATIONS AND CLEVER ZAG STYLES ARE ENDLESS:

Eg:

SHAGGY LOOK   WATERFALL   RAGGA   I'VE JUST SEEN A GHOST   SEXY LOOK

EYES: YOU MUST PRACTICE DAILY TO BECOME ZAG EYED, WHICH HAS THE DISTINCT ADVANTAGE OVER NORMAL EYES BECAUSE YOU CAN LOOK LEFT AND RIGHT, BOTH AT THE SAME TIME!
(which is very useful when you're driving in your car and there are two super-models walking on opposite sides of the road!)

COMPLEXION: PURPLE FUR WITH GREEN SPOTS - CONSULT YOUR LOCAL PLASTIC SURGEON!

ZAG-SPEAK: THIS IS A VERY IMPORTANT PART OF YOUR QUEST FOR ZAGDOM. HERE ARE A FEW KEY PHRASES YOU CAN LEARN OFF TO IMPRESS YOUR FRIENDS WITH:

HAVE AN OPINION BOY!

COOOO-EL!

R-U-SEEERIOUS!

NOW THAT'S CERTAINLY NOT PART OF THE SCHEME OF THINGS, YOUNG MAN!!

THAT'S JUST NOT THE TYPE OF WORD TO BE BANDIED 'ROUND LOOSELY!

I'M TELLING MOTHER!

THAT'S NI-SGUSTING!

The Gurls, the Gurls they all Love me!
*SUNG IN A RAGGA STYLE!

ABSO-BLOOMIN-LUTELY!

NOW YOU'RE CERTAINLY ON YOUR WAY TO BECOMING A LITTLE BIT MORE LIKE YOUR HERO! COOOOOOOOOOO-EL!

BOTTOM!!

IN EACH ONE OF US LURKS THE FEAR OF LOSING ITEMS OF CLOTHING...
AAAAAAAAAAAAAAGH!
ANORAKNAPHOBIA
A ZOG PICTURE PRESENTATION

HILARIOUS

ZAG's One liners I've said to famous People!

THAT YOU TOO CAN USE, WHEN YOU MEET YOUR FAVOURITE CELEBS!

PRINCESS DIANA: "Hi Di Hi, campers!"

DAWN FRENCH: "Bonjour Dawn!" (Geddit? It's a classic!)

RIK MAYALL: "You must get a lot of **mail, Rik!**"

DAVID BELLAMY: "Oh David, your name rings **a bell with me!**"

CHRIS EUBANK: "So, where do you bank, Chris?"

Neil kinnock: "I couldn't find the bell Neil, so I had to kinnock!"

Robbie Coletrane: "Hey look, there's a **coal train, Robbie!**"

John Cleese: "I'm very **Cleesed** to **meet you!**" (That cracked him up, that did!)

Sting: "You're a very buzzy, man!" (buzz, geddit! ha.ha!)

KIM WILDE: "You're a bit **WILD, KIM!**" (Hilarious!)

KIM WILDE ... or is it a **Moore?**" (ha.ha!)

BEN ELTON: "HOW'S YOUR BROTHER **JOHN?**" (THINK ABOUT IT, IT'S A KILLER!)

PATRICK MOORE: "Is that a large piece of swamp ground, or is it a **Moore?**" (ha.ha!)

JASON DONOVAN: "There's that new Greek mobile takeaway Jason; it's a **Doner Van!!**" (FUNNY EH!?)

ALL OF DEF LEPPARD: "WHAT? SORRY, I CAN'T HEAR A WORD YOU'RE SAYING?!" (Y'SEE, I WAS PRETENDING TO BE DEAF, GEDDIT? RIP ROARING HILARITY!)

CINDY CRAWFORD: "You're a **Doll**, Cindy!" (THINK ABOUT IT, IT'S A GOOD ONE!)

THE "ZAG IS GREAT AND I AGREE" FAN CLUB

5. EAU DE ZAG – Live the essence of ZAG. For the 90's Alien. X-CITE-MENT. **Z93**

1. ZAG TOY – This fine deluxe HAND MADE soft toy is just like the real thing. Made from BILK FUR from the planet Bill, but don't worry they were all dead before we skinned them. **Z55**

2. TEA POT – Just like Granny's. Perfect for home or the office. 100% porcelain made from RECYCLED TOILETS. **Z15**

3. FONDUE SET – Be just like foreign people and enjoy NUTRITIOUS FONDUE FOOD in this five piece set. **Z33**

4. RIBBON PASTA – To be served with any of the range of ZAG pasta sauces. **Z12**

6. TOILET ROLL – Made from 100% toilet roll. As used by ZAG. **Z3**

7. GREY MUG – Well it's just a great grey mug. **Z17**

9. BASEBALL CAP – As worn by ZAG in the movie CLIFFHANGER. **Z17**

10. ICE CREAM SCOOP – Fabulous ice cream scoop to compliment the 25 flavours of ZAG ice cream. Made from real YAK milk. **Z7**

11. TOE CHEESE GRATER – Foot problems, no problems. Used and approved by SOCKMAN and BUNION BOY! Shred those pongs away. **Z5**

12. LEATHER PATENT SHOES – Made by CHARLES DEBOUR OF SAVILLE ROW. Posh looking exclusive ZAG design. These'll put a spring in your step. **Z200**

13. CHRISTMAS CRACKER – Your Christmas party will go with a bang. Each cracker contains a fabulous FREE COMPASS! **Z3**

14. FOOT MASSAGER – After grating out that TOE CHEESE, massage those worries away with this hand crafted foot massager, carved by ZAG himself. **Z55**

ZAG GOLD CLUB CARD: Z400 annual fee

This years **GOLD CLUB** special:
CARRIBEAN CRUISE travel with Captain ZAG on his yacht CINDY – 2 weeks B&B **Z3993**

8. POT POURRI – Beautiful pine cones saved from the forests of AUSTRIA. These cones have been delicately rolled through ZAG's fur to evoke the scent and sensuousness of your favourite alien **Z29**

15. Z–FRONT UNDERPANTS – In blue or white and in two sizes only – Extra sexy and extra, extra sexy! **Z31**